G000019648

SPORT FOR THE ELDERLY

Silvey-Jex

ISBN: 9781909732254

SPORT FOR THE ELDERLY

IT'S NO GOOD, HE CAN'T GO ON... HE'S ASLEEP

"OH BAD LUCK NORMAN"

BOY, LOOK AT THE TITS ON THAT!

"...46...47...48...49..."

"ON YOUR MARKS... GET SET... THROW!"

"...AND THE RESULT OF THE URINE TEST SHOWS TRACES OF DYSPEPSIA POWDER, HEART&LIVER PILLS, IRON TABLETS & DENTURE CREAM. PRETTY DAMNING STUFF EH?"